NORDIC
DESIGNS
COLORING BOOK

JESSICA MAZURKIEWICZ

DOVER PUBLICATIONS, INC.
MINEOLA, NEW YORK

Bibliographical Note

Nordic Designs Coloring Book is a new work, first published
by Dover Publications, Inc., in 2015.

This 2015 edition printed for Barnes & Noble, Inc., by Dover Publications, Inc.

International Standard Book Number
ISBN-13: 978-0-486-79923-0

Manufactured in the United States by Courier Corporation